My First Find the
ODD ONE OUT
Book

Ruth Thomson • Illustrated by Chris McEwan

TREASURE PRESS

pets

What's the odd one out?

tasty fruit

What's the odd one out?

breakfast time

What's the odd one out?

lots of toys

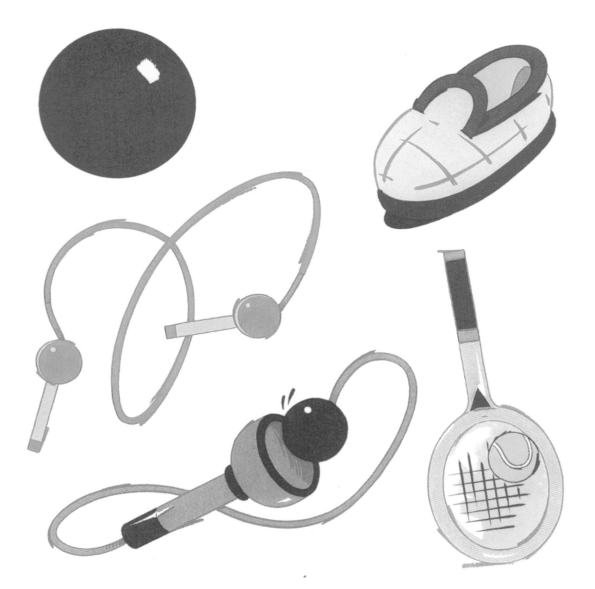

What's the odd one out?

sunny day clothes

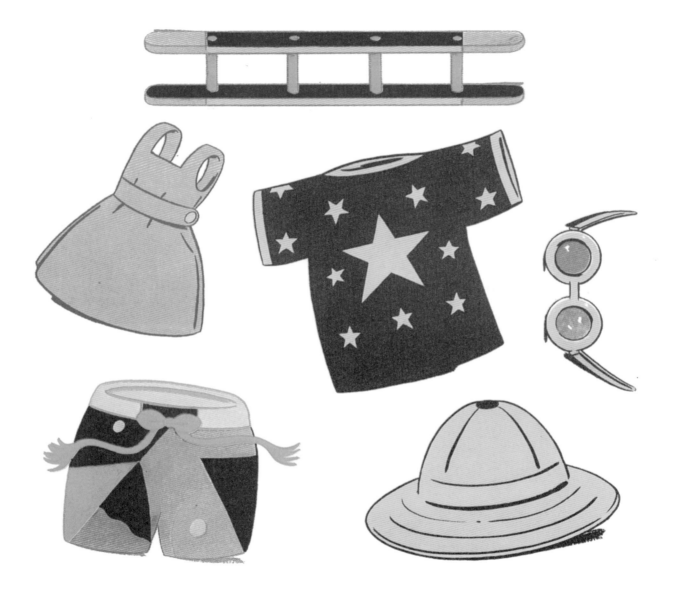

What's the odd one out?

bath time

What's the odd one out?

lovely vegetables

What's the odd one out?

creepy crawlies

What's the odd one out?

snowy weather clothes

What's the odd one out?

wheels, wheels

What's the odd one out?

party time

What's the odd one out?

up in the air

What's the odd one out?

rainy day clothes

What's the odd one out?

First published in Great Britain in 1986 by Conran Octopus Limited

This edition first published in Great Britain in 1990 by
Treasure Press
Michelin House
81 Fulham Road
London SW3 6RB

Designed by Heather Garioch
Educational consultant: Mark Evans,
Lecturer in Education (Primary)
B.A. Hons, Oxon, P.G.C.E, Lond. M.Coll.P.

ISBN 1 85051 503 4

Printed in Great Britain